# ROYAL
# CONSERVATORY OF MUSIC

University of Toronto

## GRADE VI
### PIANOFORTE
### EXAMINATION

ISBN 0-88797-036-2

529 Speers Road, Oakville, Ontario, Canada L6K 2G4

**Printed in Canada**

# FOREWORD

This book is published by the authority of the Royal Conservatory of Music, and contains compositions acceptable for the Grade VI Pianoforte Examination. However, teachers and students should check the current Syllabus in case there are changes in regulations and content. In the event of any variation between this book and the current Syllabus, the Syllabus is considered authoritative.

The editing of all pieces should be studied carefully but, particularly in the case of pieces in Lists A and B, must be considered as helpful and not arbitrary. Metronome speeds, phrasing, shading nuances, pedalling, fingering, etc., are given only as guides where the composer's own markings — which are generally considered to be essential to a good performance — are inadequate.

Editorial suggestions appear, (in some cases) in lighter print. Whenever possible comparison should be made with the "Urtext" and other editions.

Where no pedalling is indicated it does not necessarily mean that the pedals should not be used.

The Royal Conservatory of Music,
University of Toronto,
273 Bloor Street West,
Toronto, Ontario. M5S 1W2

# INDEX
## GRADE VI

# PRELUDE IN G
## No. 1 of Seven Miscellaneous Pieces

George Frederic HANDEL
(1685-1759)

Allegro (M.M. ♩ = 88-104)

Omit repeats in examinations.

# PRELUDE IN E MINOR S.941

## from Twelve Little Preludes No. 7

LIST A

Johann Sebastian BACH
(1685-1750)

Bar 10   A suggested interpretation of the ornamentation is   or

The Kellner manuscript shows a mordent rather than a trill.

Bar 21   Following the tradition of the baroque period, the Bishoff and the Bach-Gesellschaft editions place the second of the two eighths in the lower voices as if they should be played with the last note of the triplet.
As the two-against-three rhythm is used for one beat only, it may be one of the rare cases of the deliberate use of this rhythm.

Bar 21   Many editions have this trill. The Kellner manuscript has no trill.

F.H. 6675

# FANTASIA IN G MINOR

Allegro from No. 5, of "Third Dozen"

George Phillipp TELEMANN
(1681-1767)

It is advisable to be consistent in the choice of the ornamentation.

F.H. 6675

(c) Bar 32

# FANTASIA IN C MINOR

Grazioso from No. 6 "Third Dozen"

George Phillipp TELEMANN
(1681-1767)

By playing the eighth notes throughout with a mezzo-staccato touch,
the light charming character of this work will be enhanced.

Omit repeats in examinations.

F.H. 6675

# SARABANDE
Suite (Sonata) in G minor

Domenico ZIPOLI
(1688-1726)

Omit repeats in examinations.

LIST A

# TOCCATA IN E FLAT

Johann Ludwig KREBS
(1713-1780)

Allegro (M.M. ♩ = 88-108)

*without pedal*

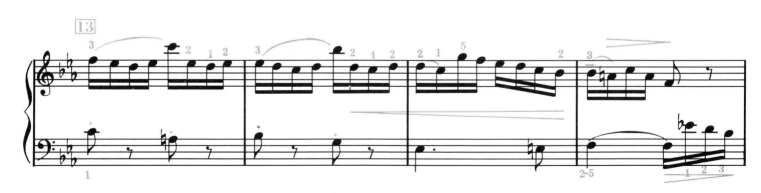

Omit repeats in examinations.

F.H. 6675

# POLONAISE IN G MINOR

from The Anna Magdalena Notebook (1725)

Johann Sebastian BACH
(1685-1750)

Maestoso (M.M.ca. ♩=60-76)

Omit repeats in examinations.

F.H. 6675

The character of this ceremonial processional dance is possibly best achieved by a non-legato touch, except where Bach himself placed the slurs, e.g. bars 4 & 22.

# SONATA IN B FLAT

(Longo 97, Kirkpatrick 440)

Tempo di minuetto (M.M.ca. ♩=100-108)

Domenico SCARLATTI
(1685-1757)

Omit repeats in examinations.

F.H. 6675

# SONATINA IN C
### Op. 20, No. 1 (First Movement)

Fr. KUHLAU
(1786-1882)

Omit repeats in examinations.

F.H. 6675

# SONATA IN D MINOR

LIST B

D. CIMAROSA
(1749-1801)

Andante (M.M.ca. ♩=66-72)

LIST B

# SONATINA
Op. 23, No. 2  (First Movement)

A. LAVIGNAC
(1846-1916)

**Allegretto** (M.M.ca. ♩=88-96)

Omit repeats in examinations.

F.H. 6675

21

F.H. 6675

# SONATA IN F, No. 5

### (Third Movement)
from First Collection for Connoisseurs and Amateurs

C.P.E. BACH
(1714-1788)

Allegretto (M.M.ca. ♩=60)

(a)

Omit repeats in examinations.

# SONATA IN A MINOR

(Longo 93)   (Kirkpatrick 149)

Domenico SCARLATTI
(1685-1757)

(a) �   (b) �   bars 14, 29, 30 similar treatment.

Omit repeats in examinations.

F.H. 6675

* When playing the repeat, start at bar 17. (2/4)

Omit repeats in examinations.

F.H. 6675

# SONATINA IN G
## Op. 55, No. 2   (Third Movement)

Fr. KUHLAU
(1786-1832)

Allegro (M.M.ca. ♩= 92-112)

LIST C

# KANGAROO
## from "Australian Suite"

George FIALA
(1921-    )

**Andantino con moto** (M.M. ♩=84)

*mf leggiero*

F.H. 6675

LIST C

For Michael Spivak
# PRELUDE 2

**Lento sostenuto**   (M.M. ♩. = ca. 40)

Srul Irving GLICK

*cantabile espressivo*

*cresc.*

F.H. 6675

# CAVALRY GALLOP

Op. 27, Bk. No. 10

Dmitri KABALEVSKY
(1904-    )

**Allegro molto**  (M.M.ca. ♩=116-132)

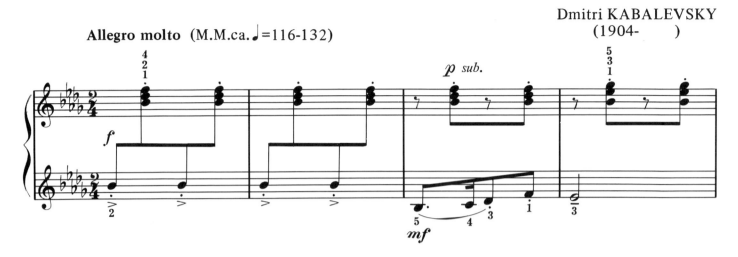

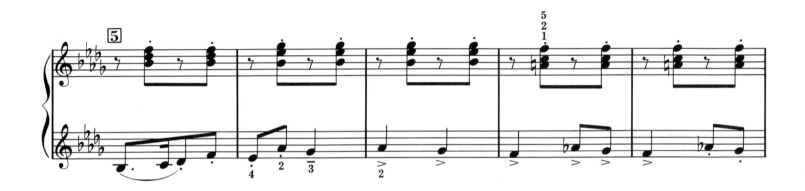

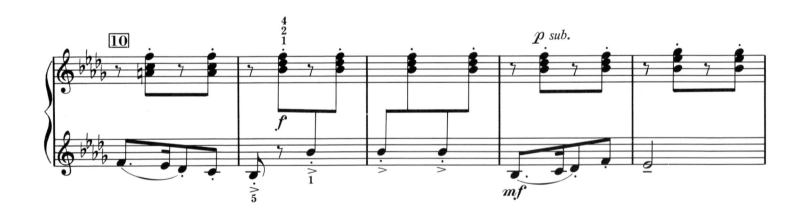

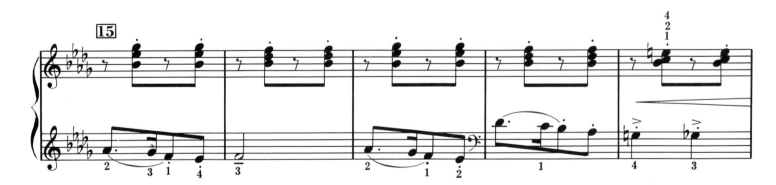

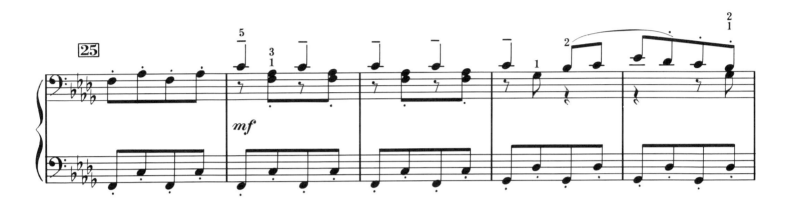

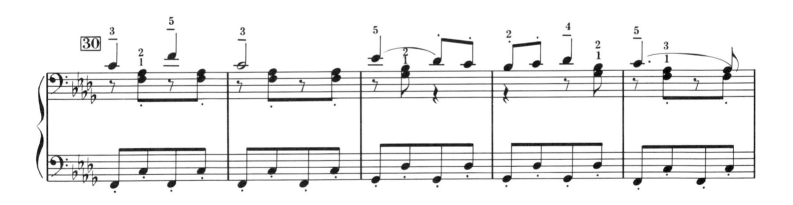

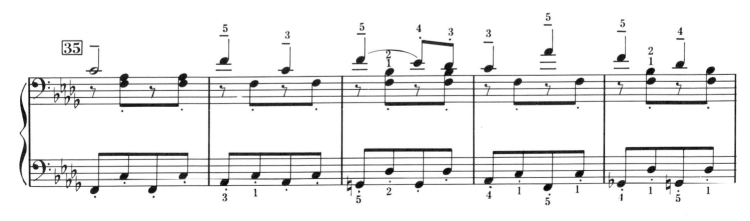

# FALLING FLAKES
## (In Children's Land)
### Op. 46, No. 14

**LIST C**

Walter NIEMANN

**Leicht und zierlich** *

*Mit recht spitzigen Schneeflocken!*

* Lightly and delicately.

F.H. 6675

# FOLK TUNE
from Lyric Pieces, Book I
Op. 12, No. 5

LIST C

Edvard GRIEG
(1843-1907)

Con moto (MM. ca. ♩ = 96)

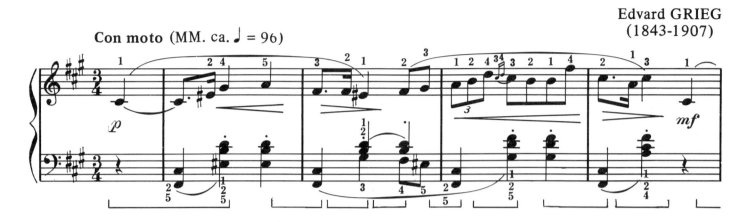

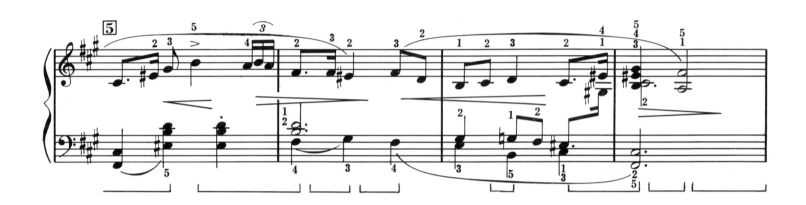

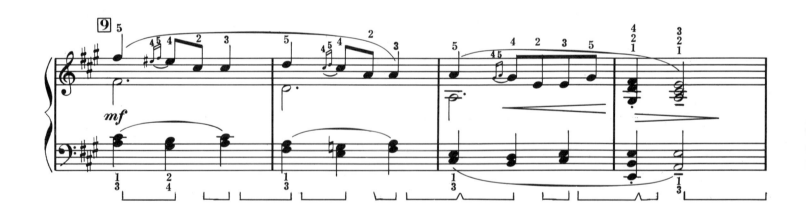

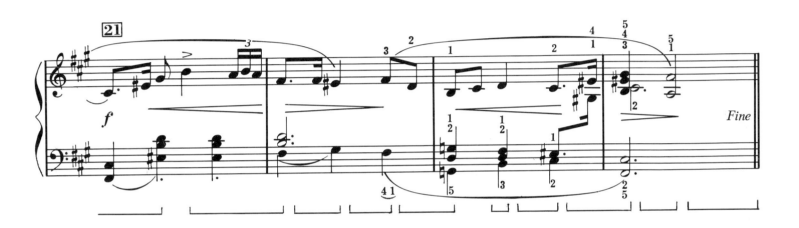

*To Sylvia*

# TOCCATA-DANCE

Poco pesante ( ♩=ca.144 )

TALIVALDIS KENINS

# VALSE IN A MINOR

## (Posthumous)

Frederick CHOPIN
(1810-1849)

Allegretto, con rubato (M.M. ♩= 104-116)

Omit repeats in examinations.

Omit repeats in examinations.

LIST C

# PLAYING MARBLES

from "Children's Festival"

Allegro brillante (M.M.ca. ♩=80-88)

Octavio PINTO
(1890-1950)

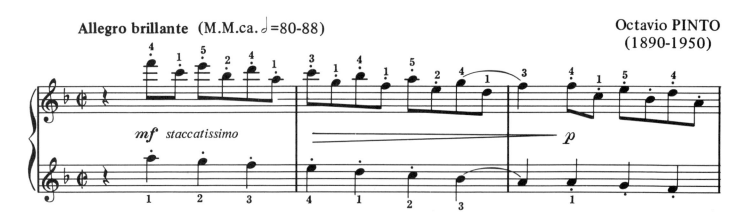

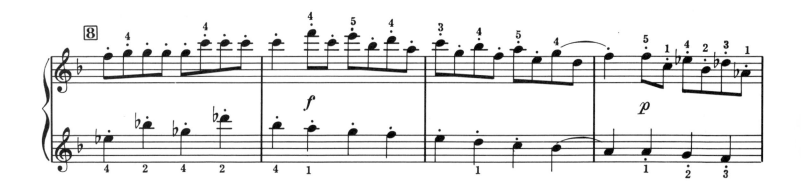

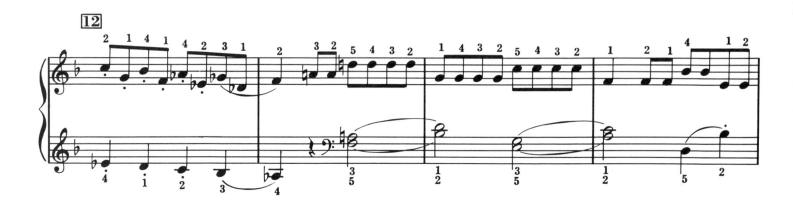

# STUDY No. 1
## Op. 47, No. 26

A. GOEDICKE
(1877-1961)

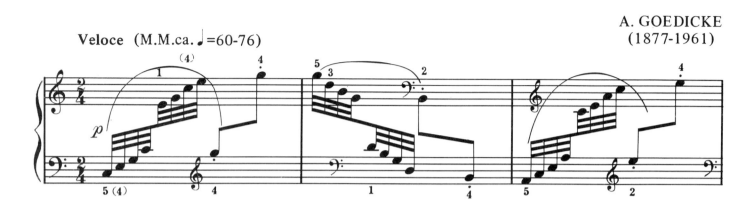

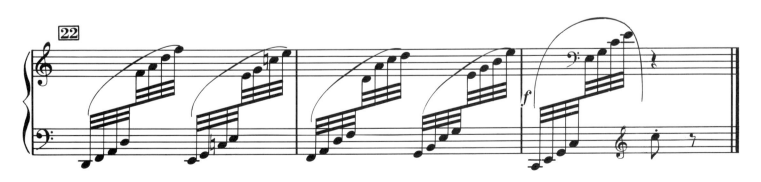

# STUDY No. 2

## Op. 88, No. 18

H. BERENS
(1826-1880)

Allegro scherzando (M.M.ca. ♩=84-92)

# STUDY No. 3

Karl CZERNY
(1791-1857)

Omit repeats in examinations.

F.H. 6675

# STUDY No. 4

## Op. 599

Karl CZERNY
(1791-1857)

Omit repeats in examinations.

F.H. 6675

# STUDY No. 5

## Op. 88, No. 6

Allegro con fuoco (M.M.ca. ♩=60-72)

H. BERENS
(1826-1880)

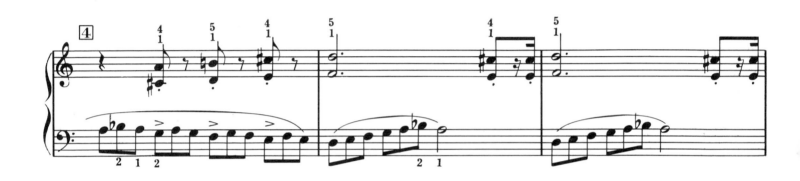

F.H. 6675

# STUDY No. 6

## Op. 37, No. 35

H. LEMOINE
(1786-1854)

(M.M.ca. ♩=63-76)

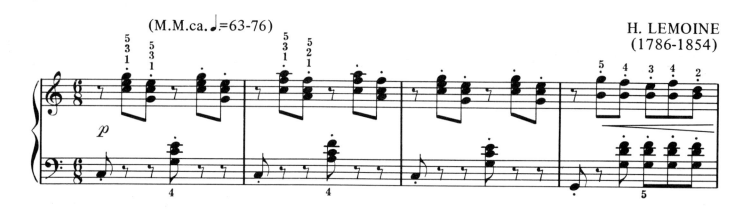

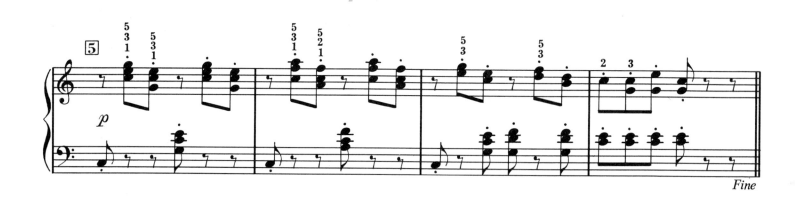

*Fine*

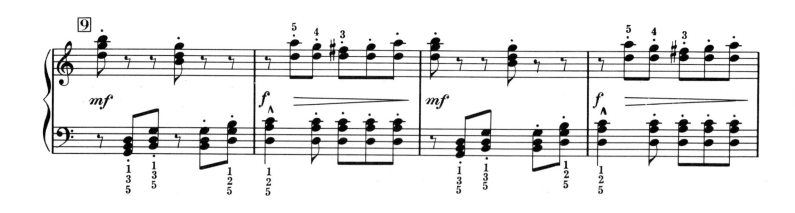

*D.C. al Fine*

# STUDY No. 7
## Op. 150, No. 19

A. BIEHL
(1870-1894)

**Andante espressivo** (M.M.ca. ♩=54-63)

# STUDY No. 8
## Op. 68, No. 6

Karl CZERNY
(1791-1857)

Allegro (M.M.ca. ♩=88)